The Ba

by Dot Meharry
illustrated by Shane Nagle

SCHOOL PUBLISHERS

Printed in China

ISBN 10: 0-15-351249-0
ISBN 13: 978-0-15-351249-0

Ordering Options
ISBN 10: 0-15-351211-3 (Grade 1 Advanced Collection)
ISBN 13: 978-0-15-351211-7 (Grade 1 Advanced Collection)
ISBN 10: 0-15-358017-8 (package of 5)
ISBN 13: 978-0-15-358017-8 (package of 5)

3 4 5 6 7 8 9 10   468   15 14 13 12 11 10 09 08

Jack is so late
for school.

Look! Jack's backpack
is up there on the rack.

Oh, no!
Jack is too little.

Can Dad help him
get the backpack?

Yes, he can help him
get the backpack.

Let's go to school now.
Go get in back, Jack.

We are here now.
We are not late
for school.